# MY
# DREAM
# JOURNAL

Roma Waterman
P O Box 288
Warrandyte, Victoria
Melbourne, Australia 3113

roma@romawaterman.com
www.romawaterman.com
training.romawaterman.com
Published by: I Was Carried Pty Ltd
Distributed by: I Was Carried Pty Ltd

ISBN: 978-0-646-85039-9

Writing, Editing & Design by Roma Waterman
Additional Editing by Emma Hunter
Formatting and pre-press by Joshua Halls at Roar Kingdom Creative
Printed in Australia

"Don't be pushed by your problems, be led by your dreams".

—Unknown

# TABLE OF CONTENTS

*Hey there dreamer,*

WELCOME TO THE REALM OF DREAMS.

NOT JUST ANY DREAMS...BUT DREAMS FROM GOD...

FOR DIRECTION, FOR FORESIGHT, FOR INSIGHT, FOR COMFORT.

'MY DREAM JOURNAL' IS A KEEPSAKE JOURNAL FOR YOU TO RECORD THE DREAMS THAT HAVE SIGNIFICANCE TO YOU.

KEEPING A RECORD OF YOUR DREAMS IS A REALLY POWERFUL WAY TO CATALOGUE WHAT THE LORD MAY BE TRYING TO SAY TO YOU.

IN THIS JOURNAL, YOU WILL FIND SPACE TO RECORD YOUR DREAMS, AND I BELIEVE THAT AS YOU BECOME INTENTIONAL IN PAYING ATTENTION, YOU WILL BEGIN TO HEAR GOD'S VOICE IN FRESH AND NEW WAYS.

MAY YOUR SLEEP BE SWEET AND YOUR REVELATION INCREASE MY FRIEND....

*Roma xx*

1

# INVENTIONS & IDEAS THAT
# CAME IN A DREAM

SEWING MACHINE
ELIAS HOWE

GOOGLE
LARRY PAGE

THEORY OF RELATIVITY
ALBERT EINSTEIN

THE PERIODIC TABLE
DMITRI MENDELEEV

IMAGINE
SONG BY PAUL MCCARTNEY

# UNDERSTANDING YOUR GOD GIVEN DREAMS

# Introduction

Before you get started, it is important first to get a Biblical foundation for dreaming and dream interpretation.

In these next few pages, I have included scriptural and practical teaching that will equip you in your dream life with the Lord and help you in using this journal effectively.

We will cover:

- Is dreaming scriptural?
- Why do we dream?
- Are all dreams a message from God?
- Common mistakes when interpreting dreams;
- Colours in dreams and their meaning;
- Numbers in dreams and their meaning;
- How to interpret other people's dreams as well as your own;
- Why keep a record of your dreams?

I have also included some practical activations, a crafted prayer for hearing from God in dreams and a recommended reading list if you would like to learn even more!

# 3 Ways God Can Speak

### *Did you know that God speaks to His people all throughout the Bible?*

It is clear from scripture that God uses dreams to speak to his people. To put this in context, Dan McCollam, in his training on dreams, suggests that the way God speaks can be one of three ways:

### *Internal*

For example, it could be an inner voice, a knowing, a feeling or a sense.

### *External*

It could be hearing someone preaching, hearing the spoken word of God, listening to a song or being ministered to in worship, as an example.

### *Mystical*

Dreaming could be considered the mystical aspect of God's communication with humanity.

# Is Dreaming Scriptural?

*There are many scriptures that speak about dreams. Here are a few:*

- Job 33:14-15 (NIV) *"For God does speak - now one way, now another - though man may not perceive it. In a dream, in a vision of the night, when deep sleep falls on men as they slumber in their beds..."*

- Genesis 46:2 (NIV) *"And God spoke to Israel in a vision at night and said, 'Jacob! Jacob!' 'Here I am,' He replied."*

- Acts 16:9 (NIV) *"During the night Paul had a vision of a man of Macedonia standing and begging him, 'come over to Macedonia and help us.'"*

- Acts 18:9 (NIV) *"One night the Lord spoke to Paul in a vision: 'don't be afraid; keep on speaking, don't be silent...'"*

- Joseph in the Old Testament was able to interpret the dreams of Pharaoh (Genesis 41) and others with great clarity. He also had dreams that foretold his future (his brothers bowing down to him and the famine that was to come to Egypt–Genesis 37)

- Joseph, the earthly father of Jesus, almost didn't marry Mary when he found out she was pregnant. A dream not only encouraged him to marry her but also kept his family safe. It is recorded in the book of Matthew that Joseph had four dreams, each time, God revealed the next steps and strategy! (Matt 1:20, Matt 2:1-12,Matt 2:16-18, Matt 2:22)

# Why Do We Dream?

- Dreams can reveal what is really going on in our hearts.

- Dreams bypass the normal 'filters' in our minds when we are awake. Sometimes those filters can stop us from hearing from God. Or another way of saying it is that we have so many other senses activated when we are awake that we don't have the 'headspace' to hear from God clearly. Adam Thompson says, "dreams bypass the hearts natural defense mechanisms and allow the Holy Spirit to bring conviction and correction".

- They can build faith. Think of Gideon (Judges 7:13-14)

- Reveals secrets and answers questions (1 Sam. 28:6)

- Warnings (Matt 2:12, Matt 2:13)

- To correct us (Job 33:14-17)

- To show us the future/prophetic (I dreamed of having a son ten years before I even knew I would have trouble falling pregnant or even wanted children!)

# Are All Dreams A Message From God?

- No, not all dreams are from God, but also consider that God will use anything to speak to you! (He will work all things together for your good (Romans 8:28).

- Some dreams can be you processing thoughts at the end of the day. (Dan McCollam calls this the 'computer clean up').

- Some dreams can be a chemical reaction to food or drugs.

- Some dreams (i.e. nightmares) are demonic in nature – this can come from the enemy trying to push against your calling, or it could be coming in through a doorway you are allowing (for example, what you are watching or engaged in, the people you hang out with etc.).

- Some people dream more than others because it's a primary receptor for how they hear from God. Just like there are different types of physical learners, there are also different types of spiritual learners (i.e. aural learner, visual learner etc.)

# Common Mistakes When Interpreting Dreams

- When you dream of a specific person, you may think the dream is about them. Sometimes in a dream however, it is more about what that person means to you or what they represent in your life. You may miss an important revelation if you automatically assume it is about one person.

- The image may not represent the image –it could be a spiritual meaning (i.e. being pregnant in a dream doesn't mean you will be pregnant).

- It's not only what you dream but also how you feel that is important during the dream and when you wake. Take that into account.

- Different symbols mean different things to different people. This is because of culture, life experience etc. This must also be taken into account when you are interpreting your own dreams and others.

# Helping Others Interpret Their Dreams

- When interpreting someone else's dreams, be careful not to ascribe your own meaning or personal experience to their symbols.

- What is more beneficial is to help people interpret their own dreams by asking them the questions in the checklist.

- If you sense a warning or something demonic or negative, it is helpful to teach people to interpret their dreams and come to their own conclusions of a dream as it means they can continue on the path of hearing God for themselves.

- If you sense this is a warning dream or demonic dream (i.e. not from God) and you do not know the person well, be sensitive and in communication with the Holy Spirit as to how to communicate this.

- If you are not experienced in this type of interpretation, help them by getting them to answer questions to help them come to their own conclusions. Using the questions in the checklist (page 40) will also be helpful.

An angel of the Lord
appeared to him in a
dream..."
– Matt 1:20

# INTERESTING FACT

"PURPLE DYE WAS DERIVED FROM THE MUREX SHELLFISH FOUND IN THE MEDITERRANEAN SEA, AND 250,000 MOLLUSKS WERE NEEDED TO MAKE ONE OUNCE OF DYE. BECAUSE PURPLE DYE WAS SO EXPENSIVE IN THE ANCIENT WORLD, IT WAS USED ONLY BY PEOPLE OF HIGH STATUS. THUS PURPLE BECAME A SYMBOL FOR POWER, WEALTH, AND ROYALTY."

HERE WE SEE AN EXAMPLE OF JEWISH CULTURE AND WHY COLOURS REPRESENT WHAT THEY DO.'

WILSON, NEIL; TAYLOR, NANCY RYKEN. THE A TO Z GUIDE TO BIBLE SIGNS AND SYMBOLS (P. 188). BAKER PUBLISHING GROUP. KINDLE EDITION.

# Colours and Numbers

*It's not just symbols that represent something in a dream. Colours and numbers are also important.*

We know this is important in Jewish culture because the Lord was specific about colours when building the temple. Each colour represented something. However, Neil Wilson and Nancy Taylor have this to say about Jewish custom in their book *"Bible Signs and Symbols"*:

*"In the ancient world, colour came through nature. The scope of colours was limited to naturally occurring hues, so things were categorized as the colour of the sky, or plants, or blood. Hebrew has only three distinct colour words and no concept or vocabulary for hue or colour variation. Most of the words translated as colour literally mean "eye," "appearance," or "aspect." Over time, certain colours became associated with specific contexts, much as the colours red and green have become associated with Christmas in the modern world. Symbolic meanings for colour evolved from their association with a context."* 2

When trying to interpret colours in a dream (and anything for that matter), we must take into account:

- Hebrew/Jewish culture
- The biblical representation of those cultures
- Our own experience and our own culture

Refer to the books mentioned in the "recommended reading" section for more context and scriptures.

# Colours & Meanings

*As a reference, here is what some colours could represent. Please check out the resource page for recommended dream dictionaries for a more exhaustive list. Also remember, colours can mean different things to different people, so also take that into account when trying to interpret their meaning.*

**BLACK**
Sin, grief, ignorance,
mourning, evil

**BLUE**
Spiritual, spiritual gift,
divine revelation,
heavenly vision,
depression (singing the blues),
prophetic

**BROWN**
Dead, repented,
born again,
without spirit

**RED**
Sin, blood shed for sin,
redemption,
passion, Holy Spirit fire

**GREY**
Unclear, undefined,
deception, hidden,
crafty, false doctrine,
wisdom (grey hair)

**GREEN**
New life, mortal, flesh, carnal,
envy, inexperienced,
mature, renewal

# Colours & Meanings

**ORANGE**
Danger, jeopardy, harm,
bright orange can represent power,
force, energy, danger

**PINK**
The flesh, sensual,
immoral, moral, chased

**PURPLE**
Royalty, ruling,
power, majestic, noble

**WHITE**
Pure, unblemished,
spotless, blameless,
truth, innocence

**YELLOW**
Cowardly,
fearful, spirit of fear,
judgement, curse, plague

# Numbers & Meanings

*The following numbers are considered symbolic and/or sacred in Judaism. This is n an exhaustive list but can help get you started in understanding numbers in you dreams.*

 Unity, wholeness, God, beginning, love, first in line

 Divide, judge, separate, discern, witness, division, multiplication, double-minded, repeat

 Completeness, stability, persistence, trinity, resurrection, fullness, Holy Spirit, perfect

 Reign, rule, kingdom, dominion on earth, creation or creative works, not enough, not known

 Grace, abundance, favour, redemption, five- fold ministry

 Human, humanity, works, not from God, independent from God

 Creation, good fortune, blessing, divine perfection, rest, spiritual completion, blessed

 Completion, new beginnings, abounding to strength, worship, resurrection, regeneration, eternity

 End, final judgement, conclusion, fruitfulness, number for Holy Spirit

 Fullness, full, complete, completion of cycle, judgment

# Numbers & Meanings

Totality, wholeness, the completion of God's purpose. There are 12 tribes of Israel, 12 months in the year, perfect government, divine organisation

Abundance. In its prime Jerusalem had 24 dream interpreters you could consult, 24 main thoroughfares with 24 side streets leading to 24 alleys each containing 24 houses (Lamentations, Rabbah I).

Fourty appears many times in the Bible, usually represnting a time of radical transition/ transformation. 40 days of flood, 40 years Iraelites in the desert, Moses spent 40 days on Mt Sinai with God, Elijah fasted 40 days etc.

Liberty, jubilee, release, freedom, deliverance, Pentecost, extreme grace

A generation (years), spiritual order, fullness of accomplishment. There are 70 nations in the world. The Greek translation of the Bible was done by 70 Jewish scholars, who, though working separately, produced 70 identical translations.

meanings are taken from the following website: Taken from: https://www.amazon.com/Encyclopedia-Jewish-Myth-Mysticism/dp/073874591X/ref=as_li_ss_tl?ie=UTF8&qid=1472071019&sr=8-words=encyclopedia+of+magic+mysticism&linkCode=sli&tag=myjewishlearn20&linkId=caea7191f60f208894692f70a61479d9

nformation on the meaning of numbers also taken from The Divinity Code by Adam Thompson and Adrian Beale, and Understanding eams you Dream by Ira Milligan, and The A to Z Guide to Bible Signs and Symbols by Wilson and Taylor . It is not exhaustive and keep in mind that cultural, historical and personal aspects need to be considered.

# CRAFTED PRAYERS
# FROM DREAMS

# From Dreams Into Crafted Prayers

A crafted prayer is an idea taken from Graeme Cooke's book *'Crafted Prayer - The Joy of Always Getting Your Prayers Answered'*. The general idea is that we can take a prophetic promise from scripture or prophetic words and turn it into specific, strategic prayers.

Taking this idea further, I believe that God can reveal a prophetic promise to you through your dreams. This idea of crafting a prayer as you listen to the Lord and praying what He wants you to pray is a compelling strategy in seeing His will manifest through your life.

The Psalms are a perfect example of crafted prayers. David, the poet and the prophet musician, pours out his heart in beautiful prose. Thousands of years later, these prayers are engraved so beautifully in the pillars of our understanding of who God is and what His promises are over us.

Graham's perception of effective prayer is so refreshing: *"Prayer is finding out what God wants to do and asking him to do it."* Finding out what God wants to do is critical in seeing our prayers answered, and crafting prayers from our God dreams is an excellent way to do this.

"For God does speak—now one way, now another—though no one perceives it. In a dream, in a vision of the night, when deep sleep falls on people as they slumber in their beds..."

– Job 33:14–15

## Start by Thanking Him

Effective prayer begins with thanking God. Psalm 100:4 says it like this: *"Enter with the password: "Thank you!" Make yourselves at home, talking praise. Thank him. Worship him". (MSG)*

Reflecting on Romans 8:28, Graham makes a stunning connection by stating, *"We thank God first in every situation because every problem we encounter comes with His provision attached to it...that promise is a deep well of provision for us."*

*"He knows us far better than we know ourselves, knows our pregnant condition, and keeps us present before God. That's why we can be so sure that every detail in our lives of love for God is worked into something good."*
*Romans 8:28 (MSG)*

As you journal your thoughts on these pages, think of some scriptures that can be attached to your promises.

And then ask the Lord some questions: *"God, what do you want to do? What is happening in this dream?"*

As you journal your thoughts and the Lord brings to mind sacred scriptures, use this information to craft a prayer that can help you actively partner with the Lord to see His promises come to pass in your life.

You will find that these types of prayers focus on the promises of God either in scripture, through prophetic words, and of course, your dreams as you discover what the Lord wants to say to you.

**How to pray for God to reveal himself through your dreams**
You may feel like the Lord does not reveal himself through your dreams or that you don't dream at all. I believe that if you desire Him to speak through your dreams, He will do it!
One of my favourite scriptures is a promise of how the Lord will speak to you if you ask Him to:

*"Call to me, and I will answer you and tell you great and unsearchable things you do not know."*
*Jeremiah 33:3 (NIV)*

*I have crafted a prayer specifically for those of you who would like to see an increase in the Lord speaking through a new season of dreaming. This is also a powerful prayer to pray if you experience nightmares or do not have a good experience of dreams. I believe as you are intentional regarding your dreams, they will increase in clarity, and you will hear God clearly as you press in to listen to His voice. You can pray before you go to sleep or during your daily prayer time.*

DEAR LORD,

I THANK YOU THAT YOU ARE ALWAYS WILLING TO SPEAK TO ME.
THANK YOU FOR USING MY DREAM LIFE TO SPEAK TO ME AND ASK
THAT YOU INCREASE THAT IN MY LIFE. HELP ME AND GUIDE ME AS I
LEARN TO HEAR FROM YOU IN THIS WAY.

REVEAL TO ME YOUR HIDDEN MEANINGS AND THE SECRETS OF YOUR
HEART.
REVEAL TO ME WHAT MAY BE HIDDEN THAT I CANNOT SEE.
REVEAL TO ME WHAT YOU DESIRE OF MY DESTINY AND FUTURE.

LORD, HELP ME TO INTERPRET AND UNDERSTAND WHAT YOU ARE
TRYING TO REVEAL TO ME. I QUIET MY HEART TO HEAR YOUR VOICE.
I ALSO ASK FATHER THAT YOU WOULD HELP ME IN INTERPRETING
DREAMS FOR OTHERS.
GIVE ME REVELATION AND UNDERSTANDING AS YOU DESIRE.

I ASK LORD THAT YOU PROTECT MY HEART, MIND, AND SOUL FROM
ANYTHING THE ENEMY MAY WANT TO THWART, INTERCEPT, OR TWIST
IN MY DREAM LIFE.
I COME AGAINST FEAR AND ANXIETY IN THIS AREA AND ONLY OPEN
MY HEART TO YOU AND YOUR VOICE.

I ASK YOU TO BE A HEDGE OF PROTECTION AROUND ME THAT
WOULD BE A FORTRESS AGAINST THE ENEMY. I DECLARE PSALM 91
OVER MY LIFE AND THAT NO EVIL SHALL COME NEAR ME, AND THAT
I WOULD NOT FEAR ANY TERROR IN THE NIGHT!

OVER THE NEXT MONTH, I COMMIT LORD TO GROW IN THIS AREA. I
DRAW CLOSE TO YOU, AND I THANK YOU FOR WHAT YOU WILL
REVEAL AND HEAL IN ME.

IN JESUS NAME, AMEN.

# Don't be pushed by your problems. Be led by your dreams.

**UNKNOWN**

# Recomended Resources

The Divinity Code – To Understanding Your Dreams and Visions – Adam Thompson & Adrian Beale

Understanding the Dreams you Dream – Ira Milligan

The A to Z Guide to Bible Signs and Symbols - Wilson, Neil; Taylor, Nancy Ryken. Baker Publishing Group. Kindle Edition.

The Tabernacle: Shadows of the Messiah David M. Levy, (Bellmawr, NJ: The Friends of Israel Gospel Ministry, 1993)

Stacey Hilliar –Dream Series Online Course (For the first few videos check out her Instagram)
https://www.instagram.com/tv/CFYyZmaHHM4/

Dream Language: The Prophetic Power of Dreams – James Goll

Exploring the Nature and Gift of Dreams: How to Understand Your Dream Language - James Goll

Crafted Prayers – The joy of always getting your prayers answered, Graham Cooke, Brilliant Bookhouse, 2015

# JOURNAL YOUR DREAMS

# How To Keep A Record Of Your Dreams

*In this section, you will find three sections for each of your dreams.*

Each dream has three pages you can use. Don't feel you have to use them all - they are there as prompts to help you understand the messages in your dreams.

### Section One

Space to write down your dream;

### Section Two

A dream Checklist. Use these questions to help you fill in page three;

### Section Three

Prompts: How you felt, What is God Saying, A scripture that might relate to your dream.

Dream Again...

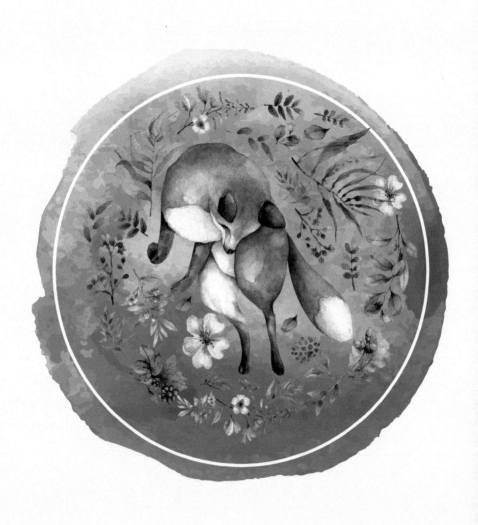

**Date:**

**Dream:**

_____

_____

_____

_____

_____

_____

_____

_____

_____

_____

_____

_____

_____

_____

_____

_____

_____

_____

_____

# DREAM CHECKLIST

## WHAT IS THE DREAM ABOUT?
### (TICK ALL THAT APPLY)

- [ ] ME
- [ ] SOMEONE ELSE
- [ ] A CORRECTION
- [ ] TO ENCOURAGE/BUILD FAITH
- [ ] REVEALING THE FUTURE
- [ ] OTHER

## SOME QUESTIONS TO ASK:

- WHAT COLOURS DID I SEE AND WHAT COULD THEY REPRESENT?

- HOW DID I FEEL WHEN I WOKE UP? HOW DID I FEEL IN THE DREAM?

- WHAT DOES THAT SYMBOLISE TO ME PERSONALLY?

- IS THERE A SCRIPTURE I CAN CONNECT TO MY DREAM?

- ARE THERE ANY REFERENCES IN SCRIPTURE TO THIS SYMBOL THAT MAY HELP ME INTERPRET MY DREAM?

- AM I SEEING THIS PATTERN IN DIFFERENT WAYS IN OTHER DREAMS OR IN EVERYDAY LIFE? WHY IS THAT?

- IS GOD TRYING TO REALLY TELL ME SOMETHING?

How I felt:

Scripture:

What is God Saying?

**Date:**

**Dream:**

# DREAM CHECKLIST

## WHAT IS THE DREAM ABOUT?
### (TICK ALL THAT APPLY)

- [ ] ME
- [ ] SOMEONE ELSE
- [ ] A CORRECTION
- [ ] TO ENCOURAGE/BUILD FAITH
- [ ] REVEALING THE FUTURE
- [ ] OTHER

## SOME QUESTIONS TO ASK:

- WHAT COLOURS DID I SEE AND WHAT COULD THEY REPRESENT?

- HOW DID I FEEL WHEN I WOKE UP? HOW DID I FEEL IN THE DREAM?

- WHAT DOES THAT SYMBOLISE TO ME PERSONALLY?

- IS THERE A SCRIPTURE I CAN CONNECT TO MY DREAM?

- ARE THERE ANY REFERENCES IN SCRIPTURE TO THIS SYMBOL THAT MAY HELP ME INTERPRET MY DREAM?

- AM I SEEING THIS PATTERN IN DIFFERENT WAYS IN OTHER DREAMS OR IN EVERYDAY LIFE? WHY IS THAT?

- IS GOD TRYING TO REALLY TELL ME SOMETHING?

How I felt:

Scripture:

What is God Saying?

**Date:**

**Dream:**

# DREAM CHECKLIST

## WHAT IS THE DREAM ABOUT?
### (TICK ALL THAT APPLY)

- ☐ ME
- ☐ SOMEONE ELSE
- ☐ A CORRECTION
- ☐ TO ENCOURAGE/BUILD FAITH
- ☐ REVEALING THE FUTURE
- ☐ OTHER

## SOME QUESTIONS TO ASK:

- WHAT COLOURS DID I SEE AND WHAT COULD THEY REPRESENT?

- HOW DID I FEEL WHEN I WOKE UP? HOW DID I FEEL IN THE DREAM?

- WHAT DOES THAT SYMBOLISE TO ME PERSONALLY?

- IS THERE A SCRIPTURE I CAN CONNECT TO MY DREAM?

- ARE THERE ANY REFERENCES IN SCRIPTURE TO THIS SYMBOL THAT MAY HELP ME INTERPRET MY DREAM?

- AM I SEEING THIS PATTERN IN DIFFERENT WAYS IN OTHER DREAMS OR IN EVERYDAY LIFE? WHY IS THAT?

- IS GOD TRYING TO REALLY TELL ME SOMETHING?

How I felt:

Scripture:

What is God Saying?

**Date:**

**Dream:**

# DREAM CHECKLIST

## WHAT IS THE DREAM ABOUT?
### (TICK ALL THAT APPLY)

- ☐ ME
- ☐ SOMEONE ELSE
- ☐ A CORRECTION
- ☐ TO ENCOURAGE/BUILD FAITH
- ☐ REVEALING THE FUTURE
- ☐ OTHER

## SOME QUESTIONS TO ASK:

- WHAT COLOURS DID I SEE AND WHAT COULD THEY REPRESENT?

- HOW DID I FEEL WHEN I WOKE UP? HOW DID I FEEL IN THE DREAM?

- WHAT DOES THAT SYMBOLISE TO ME PERSONALLY?

- IS THERE A SCRIPTURE I CAN CONNECT TO MY DREAM?

- ARE THERE ANY REFERENCES IN SCRIPTURE TO THIS SYMBOL THAT MAY HELP ME INTERPRET MY DREAM?

- AM I SEEING THIS PATTERN IN DIFFERENT WAYS IN OTHER DREAMS OR IN EVERYDAY LIFE? WHY IS THAT?

- IS GOD TRYING TO REALLY TELL ME SOMETHING?

How I felt:

Scripture:

What is God Saying?

**Date:**

**Dream:**

# DREAM CHECKLIST

## WHAT IS THE DREAM ABOUT?
### (TICK ALL THAT APPLY)

- ☐ ME
- ☐ SOMEONE ELSE
- ☐ A CORRECTION
- ☐ TO ENCOURAGE/BUILD FAITH
- ☐ REVEALING THE FUTURE
- ☐ OTHER

## SOME QUESTIONS TO ASK:

- WHAT COLOURS DID I SEE AND WHAT COULD THEY REPRESENT?

- HOW DID I FEEL WHEN I WOKE UP? HOW DID I FEEL IN THE DREAM?

- WHAT DOES THAT SYMBOLISE TO ME PERSONALLY?

- IS THERE A SCRIPTURE I CAN CONNECT TO MY DREAM?

- ARE THERE ANY REFERENCES IN SCRIPTURE TO THIS SYMBOL THAT MAY HELP ME INTERPRET MY DREAM?

- AM I SEEING THIS PATTERN IN DIFFERENT WAYS IN OTHER DREAMS OR IN EVERYDAY LIFE? WHY IS THAT?

- IS GOD TRYING TO REALLY TELL ME SOMETHING?

How I felt:

Scripture:

What is God Saying?

**Date:**

**Dream:**

# DREAM CHECKLIST

## WHAT IS THE DREAM ABOUT?
### (TICK ALL THAT APPLY)

- ☐ ME
- ☐ SOMEONE ELSE
- ☐ A CORRECTION
- ☐ TO ENCOURAGE/BUILD FAITH
- ☐ REVEALING THE FUTURE
- ☐ OTHER

## SOME QUESTIONS TO ASK:

- WHAT COLOURS DID I SEE AND WHAT COULD THEY REPRESENT?

- HOW DID I FEEL WHEN I WOKE UP? HOW DID I FEEL IN THE DREAM?

- WHAT DOES THAT SYMBOLISE TO ME PERSONALLY?

- IS THERE A SCRIPTURE I CAN CONNECT TO MY DREAM?

- ARE THERE ANY REFERENCES IN SCRIPTURE TO THIS SYMBOL THAT MAY HELP ME INTERPRET MY DREAM?

- AM I SEEING THIS PATTERN IN DIFFERENT WAYS IN OTHER DREAMS OR IN EVERYDAY LIFE? WHY IS THAT?

- IS GOD TRYING TO REALLY TELL ME SOMETHING?

How I felt:

Scripture:

What is God Saying?

**Date:**

**Dream:**

# DREAM CHECKLIST

## WHAT IS THE DREAM ABOUT?
### (TICK ALL THAT APPLY)

- ☐ ME
- ☐ SOMEONE ELSE
- ☐ A CORRECTION
- ☐ TO ENCOURAGE/BUILD FAITH
- ☐ REVEALING THE FUTURE
- ☐ OTHER

## SOME QUESTIONS TO ASK:

- WHAT COLOURS DID I SEE AND WHAT COULD THEY REPRESENT?

- HOW DID I FEEL WHEN I WOKE UP? HOW DID I FEEL IN THE DREAM?

- WHAT DOES THAT SYMBOLISE TO ME PERSONALLY?

- IS THERE A SCRIPTURE I CAN CONNECT TO MY DREAM?

- ARE THERE ANY REFERENCES IN SCRIPTURE TO THIS SYMBOL THAT MAY HELP ME INTERPRET MY DREAM?

- AM I SEEING THIS PATTERN IN DIFFERENT WAYS IN OTHER DREAMS OR IN EVERYDAY LIFE? WHY IS THAT?

- IS GOD TRYING TO REALLY TELL ME SOMETHING?

How I felt:

Scripture:

What is God Saying?

**Date:**

**Dream:**

_____
_____
_____
_____
_____
_____
_____
_____
_____
_____
_____
_____
_____
_____
_____
_____

# DREAM CHECKLIST

## WHAT IS THE DREAM ABOUT?
### (TICK ALL THAT APPLY)

- ☐ ME
- ☐ SOMEONE ELSE
- ☐ A CORRECTION
- ☐ TO ENCOURAGE/BUILD FAITH
- ☐ REVEALING THE FUTURE
- ☐ OTHER

## SOME QUESTIONS TO ASK:

- WHAT COLOURS DID I SEE AND WHAT COULD THEY REPRESENT?

- HOW DID I FEEL WHEN I WOKE UP? HOW DID I FEEL IN THE DREAM?

- WHAT DOES THAT SYMBOLISE TO ME PERSONALLY?

- IS THERE A SCRIPTURE I CAN CONNECT TO MY DREAM?

- ARE THERE ANY REFERENCES IN SCRIPTURE TO THIS SYMBOL THAT MAY HELP ME INTERPRET MY DREAM?

- AM I SEEING THIS PATTERN IN DIFFERENT WAYS IN OTHER DREAMS OR IN EVERYDAY LIFE? WHY IS THAT?

- IS GOD TRYING TO REALLY TELL ME SOMETHING?

How I felt:

Scripture:

What is God Saying?

Date:

Dream:

_____
_____
_____
_____
_____
_____
_____
_____
_____
_____
_____
_____
_____
_____
_____
_____
_____
_____

# DREAM CHECKLIST

## WHAT IS THE DREAM ABOUT?
### (TICK ALL THAT APPLY)

- ☐ ME
- ☐ SOMEONE ELSE
- ☐ A CORRECTION
- ☐ TO ENCOURAGE/BUILD FAITH
- ☐ REVEALING THE FUTURE
- ☐ OTHER

## SOME QUESTIONS TO ASK:

- WHAT COLOURS DID I SEE AND WHAT COULD THEY REPRESENT?

- HOW DID I FEEL WHEN I WOKE UP? HOW DID I FEEL IN THE DREAM?

- WHAT DOES THAT SYMBOLISE TO ME PERSONALLY?

- IS THERE A SCRIPTURE I CAN CONNECT TO MY DREAM?

- ARE THERE ANY REFERENCES IN SCRIPTURE TO THIS SYMBOL THAT MAY HELP ME INTERPRET MY DREAM?

- AM I SEEING THIS PATTERN IN DIFFERENT WAYS IN OTHER DREAMS OR IN EVERYDAY LIFE? WHY IS THAT?

- IS GOD TRYING TO REALLY TELL ME SOMETHING?

How I felt:

Scripture:

What is God Saying?

"Listen to my words: "When there is a prophet among you, I, the Lord, reveal myself to them in visions, I speak to them in dreams."

– Numbers 12:6

**Date:**

**Dream:**

_____
_____
_____
_____
_____
_____
_____
_____
_____
_____
_____
_____
_____
_____
_____
_____
_____
_____
_____
_____

# DREAM CHECKLIST

## WHAT IS THE DREAM ABOUT?
### (TICK ALL THAT APPLY)

- ☐ ME
- ☐ SOMEONE ELSE
- ☐ A CORRECTION
- ☐ TO ENCOURAGE/BUILD FAITH
- ☐ REVEALING THE FUTURE
- ☐ OTHER

## SOME QUESTIONS TO ASK:

- WHAT COLOURS DID I SEE AND WHAT COULD THEY REPRESENT?

- HOW DID I FEEL WHEN I WOKE UP? HOW DID I FEEL IN THE DREAM?

- WHAT DOES THAT SYMBOLISE TO ME PERSONALLY?

- IS THERE A SCRIPTURE I CAN CONNECT TO MY DREAM?

- ARE THERE ANY REFERENCES IN SCRIPTURE TO THIS SYMBOL THAT MAY HELP ME INTERPRET MY DREAM?

- AM I SEEING THIS PATTERN IN DIFFERENT WAYS IN OTHER DREAMS OR IN EVERYDAY LIFE? WHY IS THAT?

- IS GOD TRYING TO REALLY TELL ME SOMETHING?

How I felt:

Scripture:

What is God Saying?

Date:

Dream:

_____
_____
_____
_____
_____
_____
_____
_____
_____
_____
_____
_____
_____
_____
_____

# DREAM CHECKLIST

## WHAT IS THE DREAM ABOUT?
### (TICK ALL THAT APPLY)

- ☐ ME
- ☐ SOMEONE ELSE
- ☐ A CORRECTION
- ☐ TO ENCOURAGE/BUILD FAITH
- ☐ REVEALING THE FUTURE
- ☐ OTHER

## SOME QUESTIONS TO ASK:

- WHAT COLOURS DID I SEE AND WHAT COULD THEY REPRESENT?

- HOW DID I FEEL WHEN I WOKE UP? HOW DID I FEEL IN THE DREAM?

- WHAT DOES THAT SYMBOLISE TO ME PERSONALLY?

- IS THERE A SCRIPTURE I CAN CONNECT TO MY DREAM?

- ARE THERE ANY REFERENCES IN SCRIPTURE TO THIS SYMBOL THAT MAY HELP ME INTERPRET MY DREAM?

- AM I SEEING THIS PATTERN IN DIFFERENT WAYS IN OTHER DREAMS OR IN EVERYDAY LIFE? WHY IS THAT?

- IS GOD TRYING TO REALLY TELL ME SOMETHING?

How I felt:

Scripture:

What is God Saying?

**Date:**

**Dream:**

_____

_____

_____

_____

_____

_____

_____

_____

_____

_____

_____

_____

_____

_____

_____

_____

_____

# DREAM CHECKLIST

## WHAT IS THE DREAM ABOUT?
### (TICK ALL THAT APPLY)

- ☐ ME
- ☐ SOMEONE ELSE
- ☐ A CORRECTION
- ☐ TO ENCOURAGE/BUILD FAITH
- ☐ REVEALING THE FUTURE
- ☐ OTHER

## SOME QUESTIONS TO ASK:

- WHAT COLOURS DID I SEE AND WHAT COULD THEY REPRESENT?

- HOW DID I FEEL WHEN I WOKE UP? HOW DID I FEEL IN THE DREAM?

- WHAT DOES THAT SYMBOLISE TO ME PERSONALLY?

- IS THERE A SCRIPTURE I CAN CONNECT TO MY DREAM?

- ARE THERE ANY REFERENCES IN SCRIPTURE TO THIS SYMBOL THAT MAY HELP ME INTERPRET MY DREAM?

- AM I SEEING THIS PATTERN IN DIFFERENT WAYS IN OTHER DREAMS OR IN EVERYDAY LIFE? WHY IS THAT?

- IS GOD TRYING TO REALLY TELL ME SOMETHING?

How I felt:

Scripture:

What is God Saying?

**Date:**

**Dream:**

# DREAM CHECKLIST

## WHAT IS THE DREAM ABOUT?
### (TICK ALL THAT APPLY)

- ☐ ME
- ☐ SOMEONE ELSE
- ☐ A CORRECTION
- ☐ TO ENCOURAGE/BUILD FAITH
- ☐ REVEALING THE FUTURE
- ☐ OTHER

## SOME QUESTIONS TO ASK:

- WHAT COLOURS DID I SEE AND WHAT COULD THEY REPRESENT?

- HOW DID I FEEL WHEN I WOKE UP? HOW DID I FEEL IN THE DREAM?

- WHAT DOES THAT SYMBOLISE TO ME PERSONALLY?

- IS THERE A SCRIPTURE I CAN CONNECT TO MY DREAM?

- ARE THERE ANY REFERENCES IN SCRIPTURE TO THIS SYMBOL THAT MAY HELP ME INTERPRET MY DREAM?

- AM I SEEING THIS PATTERN IN DIFFERENT WAYS IN OTHER DREAMS OR IN EVERYDAY LIFE? WHY IS THAT?

- IS GOD TRYING TO REALLY TELL ME SOMETHING?

How I felt:

Scripture:

What is God Saying?

**Date:**

**Dream:**

_____

_____

_____

_____

_____

_____

_____

_____

_____

_____

_____

_____

_____

_____

_____

_____

_____

_____

# DREAM CHECKLIST

## WHAT IS THE DREAM ABOUT?
## (TICK ALL THAT APPLY)

- ☐ ME
- ☐ SOMEONE ELSE
- ☐ A CORRECTION
- ☐ TO ENCOURAGE/BUILD FAITH
- ☐ REVEALING THE FUTURE
- ☐ OTHER

## SOME QUESTIONS TO ASK:

- WHAT COLOURS DID I SEE AND WHAT COULD THEY REPRESENT?

- HOW DID I FEEL WHEN I WOKE UP? HOW DID I FEEL IN THE DREAM?

- WHAT DOES THAT SYMBOLISE TO ME PERSONALLY?

- IS THERE A SCRIPTURE I CAN CONNECT TO MY DREAM?

- ARE THERE ANY REFERENCES IN SCRIPTURE TO THIS SYMBOL THAT MAY HELP ME INTERPRET MY DREAM?

- AM I SEEING THIS PATTERN IN DIFFERENT WAYS IN OTHER DREAMS OR IN EVERYDAY LIFE? WHY IS THAT?

- IS GOD TRYING TO REALLY TELL ME SOMETHING?

How I felt:

Scripture:

What is God Saying?

Date:

Dream:

_____

_____

_____

_____

_____

_____

_____

_____

_____

_____

_____

_____

_____

_____

_____

# DREAM CHECKLIST

## WHAT IS THE DREAM ABOUT?
### (TICK ALL THAT APPLY)

- [ ] ME
- [ ] SOMEONE ELSE
- [ ] A CORRECTION
- [ ] TO ENCOURAGE/BUILD FAITH
- [ ] REVEALING THE FUTURE
- [ ] OTHER

## SOME QUESTIONS TO ASK:

- WHAT COLOURS DID I SEE AND WHAT COULD THEY REPRESENT?

- HOW DID I FEEL WHEN I WOKE UP? HOW DID I FEEL IN THE DREAM?

- WHAT DOES THAT SYMBOLISE TO ME PERSONALLY?

- IS THERE A SCRIPTURE I CAN CONNECT TO MY DREAM?

- ARE THERE ANY REFERENCES IN SCRIPTURE TO THIS SYMBOL THAT MAY HELP ME INTERPRET MY DREAM?

- AM I SEEING THIS PATTERN IN DIFFERENT WAYS IN OTHER DREAMS OR IN EVERYDAY LIFE? WHY IS THAT?

- IS GOD TRYING TO REALLY TELL ME SOMETHING?

How I felt:

Scripture:

What is God Saying?

**Date:**

**Dream:**

_____
_____
_____
_____
_____
_____
_____
_____
_____
_____
_____
_____
_____
_____
_____
_____
_____

# DREAM CHECKLIST

## WHAT IS THE DREAM ABOUT?
### (TICK ALL THAT APPLY)

- ☐ ME
- ☐ SOMEONE ELSE
- ☐ A CORRECTION
- ☐ TO ENCOURAGE/BUILD FAITH
- ☐ REVEALING THE FUTURE
- ☐ OTHER

## SOME QUESTIONS TO ASK:

- WHAT COLOURS DID I SEE AND WHAT COULD THEY REPRESENT?

- HOW DID I FEEL WHEN I WOKE UP? HOW DID I FEEL IN THE DREAM?

- WHAT DOES THAT SYMBOLISE TO ME PERSONALLY?

- IS THERE A SCRIPTURE I CAN CONNECT TO MY DREAM?

- ARE THERE ANY REFERENCES IN SCRIPTURE TO THIS SYMBOL THAT MAY HELP ME INTERPRET MY DREAM?

- AM I SEEING THIS PATTERN IN DIFFERENT WAYS IN OTHER DREAMS OR IN EVERYDAY LIFE? WHY IS THAT?

- IS GOD TRYING TO REALLY TELL ME SOMETHING?

How I felt:

Scripture:

What is God Saying?

**Date:**

**Dream:**

# DREAM CHECKLIST

## WHAT IS THE DREAM ABOUT?
### (TICK ALL THAT APPLY)

- ☐ ME
- ☐ SOMEONE ELSE
- ☐ A CORRECTION
- ☐ TO ENCOURAGE/BUILD FAITH
- ☐ REVEALING THE FUTURE
- ☐ OTHER

## SOME QUESTIONS TO ASK:

- WHAT COLOURS DID I SEE AND WHAT COULD THEY REPRESENT?

- HOW DID I FEEL WHEN I WOKE UP? HOW DID I FEEL IN THE DREAM?

- WHAT DOES THAT SYMBOLISE TO ME PERSONALLY?

- IS THERE A SCRIPTURE I CAN CONNECT TO MY DREAM?

- ARE THERE ANY REFERENCES IN SCRIPTURE TO THIS SYMBOL THAT MAY HELP ME INTERPRET MY DREAM?

- AM I SEEING THIS PATTERN IN DIFFERENT WAYS IN OTHER DREAMS OR IN EVERYDAY LIFE? WHY IS THAT?

- IS GOD TRYING TO REALLY TELL ME SOMETHING?

How I felt:

Scripture:

What is God Saying?

Date:

Dream:

_____
_____
_____
_____
_____
_____
_____
_____
_____
_____
_____
_____
_____
_____
_____
_____
_____

# DREAM CHECKLIST

## WHAT IS THE DREAM ABOUT?
### (TICK ALL THAT APPLY)

- ☐ ME
- ☐ SOMEONE ELSE
- ☐ A CORRECTION
- ☐ TO ENCOURAGE/BUILD FAITH
- ☐ REVEALING THE FUTURE
- ☐ OTHER

## SOME QUESTIONS TO ASK:

- WHAT COLOURS DID I SEE AND WHAT COULD THEY REPRESENT?

- HOW DID I FEEL WHEN I WOKE UP? HOW DID I FEEL IN THE DREAM?

- WHAT DOES THAT SYMBOLISE TO ME PERSONALLY?

- IS THERE A SCRIPTURE I CAN CONNECT TO MY DREAM?

- ARE THERE ANY REFERENCES IN SCRIPTURE TO THIS SYMBOL THAT MAY HELP ME INTERPRET MY DREAM?

- AM I SEEING THIS PATTERN IN DIFFERENT WAYS IN OTHER DREAMS OR IN EVERYDAY LIFE? WHY IS THAT?

- IS GOD TRYING TO REALLY TELL ME SOMETHING?

How I felt:

Scripture:

What is God Saying?

**Date:**

**Dream:**

_____
_____
_____
_____
_____
_____
_____
_____
_____
_____
_____
_____
_____
_____
_____
_____
_____
_____

# DREAM CHECKLIST

## WHAT IS THE DREAM ABOUT?
### (TICK ALL THAT APPLY)

- [ ] ME
- [ ] SOMEONE ELSE
- [ ] A CORRECTION
- [ ] TO ENCOURAGE/BUILD FAITH
- [ ] REVEALING THE FUTURE
- [ ] OTHER

## SOME QUESTIONS TO ASK:

- WHAT COLOURS DID I SEE AND WHAT COULD THEY REPRESENT?

- HOW DID I FEEL WHEN I WOKE UP? HOW DID I FEEL IN THE DREAM?

- WHAT DOES THAT SYMBOLISE TO ME PERSONALLY?

- IS THERE A SCRIPTURE I CAN CONNECT TO MY DREAM?

- ARE THERE ANY REFERENCES IN SCRIPTURE TO THIS SYMBOL THAT MAY HELP ME INTERPRET MY DREAM?

- AM I SEEING THIS PATTERN IN DIFFERENT WAYS IN OTHER DREAMS OR IN EVERYDAY LIFE? WHY IS THAT?

- IS GOD TRYING TO REALLY TELL ME SOMETHING?

How I felt:

Scripture:

What is God Saying?

**Date:**

**Dream:**

# DREAM CHECKLIST

## WHAT IS THE DREAM ABOUT?
### (TICK ALL THAT APPLY)

- [ ] ME
- [ ] SOMEONE ELSE
- [ ] A CORRECTION
- [ ] TO ENCOURAGE/BUILD FAITH
- [ ] REVEALING THE FUTURE
- [ ] OTHER

## SOME QUESTIONS TO ASK:

- WHAT COLOURS DID I SEE AND WHAT COULD THEY REPRESENT?

- HOW DID I FEEL WHEN I WOKE UP? HOW DID I FEEL IN THE DREAM?

- WHAT DOES THAT SYMBOLISE TO ME PERSONALLY?

- IS THERE A SCRIPTURE I CAN CONNECT TO MY DREAM?

- ARE THERE ANY REFERENCES IN SCRIPTURE TO THIS SYMBOL THAT MAY HELP ME INTERPRET MY DREAM?

- AM I SEEING THIS PATTERN IN DIFFERENT WAYS IN OTHER DREAMS OR IN EVERYDAY LIFE? WHY IS THAT?

- IS GOD TRYING TO REALLY TELL ME SOMETHING?

How I felt:

Scripture:

What is God Saying?

**Date:**

**Dream:**

_____
_____
_____
_____
_____
_____
_____
_____
_____
_____
_____
_____
_____
_____
_____
_____
_____
_____
_____

# DREAM CHECKLIST

## WHAT IS THE DREAM ABOUT?
### (TICK ALL THAT APPLY)

- ☐ ME
- ☐ SOMEONE ELSE
- ☐ A CORRECTION
- ☐ TO ENCOURAGE/BUILD FAITH
- ☐ REVEALING THE FUTURE
- ☐ OTHER

## SOME QUESTIONS TO ASK:

- WHAT COLOURS DID I SEE AND WHAT COULD THEY REPRESENT?

- HOW DID I FEEL WHEN I WOKE UP? HOW DID I FEEL IN THE DREAM?

- WHAT DOES THAT SYMBOLISE TO ME PERSONALLY?

- IS THERE A SCRIPTURE I CAN CONNECT TO MY DREAM?

- ARE THERE ANY REFERENCES IN SCRIPTURE TO THIS SYMBOL THAT MAY HELP ME INTERPRET MY DREAM?

- AM I SEEING THIS PATTERN IN DIFFERENT WAYS IN OTHER DREAMS OR IN EVERYDAY LIFE? WHY IS THAT?

- IS GOD TRYING TO REALLY TELL ME SOMETHING?

How I felt:

Scripture:

What is God Saying?

**Date:**

**Dream:**

_____
_____
_____
_____
_____
_____
_____
_____
_____
_____
_____
_____
_____
_____
_____
_____
_____
_____
_____

# DREAM CHECKLIST

## WHAT IS THE DREAM ABOUT?
### (TICK ALL THAT APPLY)

- [ ] ME
- [ ] SOMEONE ELSE
- [ ] A CORRECTION
- [ ] TO ENCOURAGE/BUILD FAITH
- [ ] REVEALING THE FUTURE
- [ ] OTHER

## SOME QUESTIONS TO ASK:

- WHAT COLOURS DID I SEE AND WHAT COULD THEY REPRESENT?

- HOW DID I FEEL WHEN I WOKE UP? HOW DID I FEEL IN THE DREAM?

- WHAT DOES THAT SYMBOLISE TO ME PERSONALLY?

- IS THERE A SCRIPTURE I CAN CONNECT TO MY DREAM?

- ARE THERE ANY REFERENCES IN SCRIPTURE TO THIS SYMBOL THAT MAY HELP ME INTERPRET MY DREAM?

- AM I SEEING THIS PATTERN IN DIFFERENT WAYS IN OTHER DREAMS OR IN EVERYDAY LIFE? WHY IS THAT?

- IS GOD TRYING TO REALLY TELL ME SOMETHING?

How I felt:

Scripture:

What is God Saying?

**Date:**

**Dream:**

_____
_____
_____
_____
_____
_____
_____
_____
_____
_____
_____
_____
_____
_____
_____
_____
_____
_____
_____

# DREAM CHECKLIST

## WHAT IS THE DREAM ABOUT?
## (TICK ALL THAT APPLY)

- [ ] ME
- [ ] SOMEONE ELSE
- [ ] A CORRECTION
- [ ] TO ENCOURAGE/BUILD FAITH
- [ ] REVEALING THE FUTURE
- [ ] OTHER

## SOME QUESTIONS TO ASK:

- WHAT COLOURS DID I SEE AND WHAT COULD THEY REPRESENT?

- HOW DID I FEEL WHEN I WOKE UP? HOW DID I FEEL IN THE DREAM?

- WHAT DOES THAT SYMBOLISE TO ME PERSONALLY?

- IS THERE A SCRIPTURE I CAN CONNECT TO MY DREAM?

- ARE THERE ANY REFERENCES IN SCRIPTURE TO THIS SYMBOL THAT MAY HELP ME INTERPRET MY DREAM?

- AM I SEEING THIS PATTERN IN DIFFERENT WAYS IN OTHER DREAMS OR IN EVERYDAY LIFE? WHY IS THAT?

- IS GOD TRYING TO REALLY TELL ME SOMETHING?

How I felt:

Scripture:

What is God Saying?

**Date:**

**Dream:**

# DREAM CHECKLIST

## WHAT IS THE DREAM ABOUT?
### (TICK ALL THAT APPLY)

- ☐ ME
- ☐ SOMEONE ELSE
- ☐ A CORRECTION
- ☐ TO ENCOURAGE/BUILD FAITH
- ☐ REVEALING THE FUTURE
- ☐ OTHER

## SOME QUESTIONS TO ASK:

- WHAT COLOURS DID I SEE AND WHAT COULD THEY REPRESENT?

- HOW DID I FEEL WHEN I WOKE UP? HOW DID I FEEL IN THE DREAM?

- WHAT DOES THAT SYMBOLISE TO ME PERSONALLY?

- IS THERE A SCRIPTURE I CAN CONNECT TO MY DREAM?

- ARE THERE ANY REFERENCES IN SCRIPTURE TO THIS SYMBOL THAT MAY HELP ME INTERPRET MY DREAM?

- AM I SEEING THIS PATTERN IN DIFFERENT WAYS IN OTHER DREAMS OR IN EVERYDAY LIFE? WHY IS THAT?

- IS GOD TRYING TO REALLY TELL ME SOMETHING?

How I felt:

Scripture:

What is God Saying?

**Date:**

**Dream:**

_____

_____

_____

_____

_____

_____

_____

_____

_____

_____

_____

_____

_____

_____

_____

_____

_____

_____

# DREAM CHECKLIST

## WHAT IS THE DREAM ABOUT?
## (TICK ALL THAT APPLY)

- ☐ ME
- ☐ SOMEONE ELSE
- ☐ A CORRECTION
- ☐ TO ENCOURAGE/BUILD FAITH
- ☐ REVEALING THE FUTURE
- ☐ OTHER

## SOME QUESTIONS TO ASK:

- WHAT COLOURS DID I SEE AND WHAT COULD THEY REPRESENT?

- HOW DID I FEEL WHEN I WOKE UP? HOW DID I FEEL IN THE DREAM?

- WHAT DOES THAT SYMBOLISE TO ME PERSONALLY?

- IS THERE A SCRIPTURE I CAN CONNECT TO MY DREAM?

- ARE THERE ANY REFERENCES IN SCRIPTURE TO THIS SYMBOL THAT MAY HELP ME INTERPRET MY DREAM?

- AM I SEEING THIS PATTERN IN DIFFERENT WAYS IN OTHER DREAMS OR IN EVERYDAY LIFE? WHY IS THAT?

- IS GOD TRYING TO REALLY TELL ME SOMETHING?

How I felt:

Scripture:

What is God Saying?

Date:

Dream:

_____
_____
_____
_____
_____
_____
_____
_____
_____
_____
_____
_____
_____
_____
_____
_____
_____
_____
_____
_____
_____
_____

# DREAM CHECKLIST

## WHAT IS THE DREAM ABOUT?
### (TICK ALL THAT APPLY)

- ☐ ME
- ☐ SOMEONE ELSE
- ☐ A CORRECTION
- ☐ TO ENCOURAGE/BUILD FAITH
- ☐ REVEALING THE FUTURE
- ☐ OTHER

## SOME QUESTIONS TO ASK:

- WHAT COLOURS DID I SEE AND WHAT COULD THEY REPRESENT?

- HOW DID I FEEL WHEN I WOKE UP? HOW DID I FEEL IN THE DREAM?

- WHAT DOES THAT SYMBOLISE TO ME PERSONALLY?

- IS THERE A SCRIPTURE I CAN CONNECT TO MY DREAM?

- ARE THERE ANY REFERENCES IN SCRIPTURE TO THIS SYMBOL THAT MAY HELP ME INTERPRET MY DREAM?

- AM I SEEING THIS PATTERN IN DIFFERENT WAYS IN OTHER DREAMS OR IN EVERYDAY LIFE? WHY IS THAT?

- IS GOD TRYING TO REALLY TELL ME SOMETHING?

How I felt:

Scripture:

What is God Saying?

Date:

Dream:

_____
_____
_____
_____
_____
_____
_____
_____
_____
_____
_____
_____
_____
_____
_____
_____
_____
_____
_____

# DREAM CHECKLIST

## WHAT IS THE DREAM ABOUT?
## (TICK ALL THAT APPLY)

- ☐ ME
- ☐ SOMEONE ELSE
- ☐ A CORRECTION
- ☐ TO ENCOURAGE/BUILD FAITH
- ☐ REVEALING THE FUTURE
- ☐ OTHER

## SOME QUESTIONS TO ASK:

- WHAT COLOURS DID I SEE AND WHAT COULD THEY REPRESENT?

- HOW DID I FEEL WHEN I WOKE UP? HOW DID I FEEL IN THE DREAM?

- WHAT DOES THAT SYMBOLISE TO ME PERSONALLY?

- IS THERE A SCRIPTURE I CAN CONNECT TO MY DREAM?

- ARE THERE ANY REFERENCES IN SCRIPTURE TO THIS SYMBOL THAT MAY HELP ME INTERPRET MY DREAM?

- AM I SEEING THIS PATTERN IN DIFFERENT WAYS IN OTHER DREAMS OR IN EVERYDAY LIFE? WHY IS THAT?

- IS GOD TRYING TO REALLY TELL ME SOMETHING?

How I felt:

Scripture:

What is God Saying?

**Date:**

**Dream:**

# DREAM CHECKLIST

## WHAT IS THE DREAM ABOUT?
### (TICK ALL THAT APPLY)

- ☐ ME
- ☐ SOMEONE ELSE
- ☐ A CORRECTION
- ☐ TO ENCOURAGE/BUILD FAITH
- ☐ REVEALING THE FUTURE
- ☐ OTHER

## SOME QUESTIONS TO ASK:

- WHAT COLOURS DID I SEE AND WHAT COULD THEY REPRESENT?

- HOW DID I FEEL WHEN I WOKE UP? HOW DID I FEEL IN THE DREAM?

- WHAT DOES THAT SYMBOLISE TO ME PERSONALLY?

- IS THERE A SCRIPTURE I CAN CONNECT TO MY DREAM?

- ARE THERE ANY REFERENCES IN SCRIPTURE TO THIS SYMBOL THAT MAY HELP ME INTERPRET MY DREAM?

- AM I SEEING THIS PATTERN IN DIFFERENT WAYS IN OTHER DREAMS OR IN EVERYDAY LIFE? WHY IS THAT?

- IS GOD TRYING TO REALLY TELL ME SOMETHING?

How I felt:

Scripture:

What is God Saying?

**Date:**

**Dream:**

_____

_____

_____

_____

_____

_____

_____

_____

_____

_____

_____

_____

_____

_____

_____

_____

_____

# DREAM CHECKLIST

## WHAT IS THE DREAM ABOUT?
### (TICK ALL THAT APPLY)

- ☐ ME
- ☐ SOMEONE ELSE
- ☐ A CORRECTION
- ☐ TO ENCOURAGE/BUILD FAITH
- ☐ REVEALING THE FUTURE
- ☐ OTHER

## SOME QUESTIONS TO ASK:

- WHAT COLOURS DID I SEE AND WHAT COULD THEY REPRESENT?

- HOW DID I FEEL WHEN I WOKE UP? HOW DID I FEEL IN THE DREAM?

- WHAT DOES THAT SYMBOLISE TO ME PERSONALLY?

- IS THERE A SCRIPTURE I CAN CONNECT TO MY DREAM?

- ARE THERE ANY REFERENCES IN SCRIPTURE TO THIS SYMBOL THAT MAY HELP ME INTERPRET MY DREAM?

- AM I SEEING THIS PATTERN IN DIFFERENT WAYS IN OTHER DREAMS OR IN EVERYDAY LIFE? WHY IS THAT?

- IS GOD TRYING TO REALLY TELL ME SOMETHING?

How I felt:

Scripture:

What is God Saying?

**Date:**

**Dream:**

# DREAM CHECKLIST

## WHAT IS THE DREAM ABOUT?
### (TICK ALL THAT APPLY)

- ☐ ME
- ☐ SOMEONE ELSE
- ☐ A CORRECTION
- ☐ TO ENCOURAGE/BUILD FAITH
- ☐ REVEALING THE FUTURE
- ☐ OTHER

## SOME QUESTIONS TO ASK:

- WHAT COLOURS DID I SEE AND WHAT COULD THEY REPRESENT?

- HOW DID I FEEL WHEN I WOKE UP? HOW DID I FEEL IN THE DREAM?

- WHAT DOES THAT SYMBOLISE TO ME PERSONALLY?

- IS THERE A SCRIPTURE I CAN CONNECT TO MY DREAM?

- ARE THERE ANY REFERENCES IN SCRIPTURE TO THIS SYMBOL THAT MAY HELP ME INTERPRET MY DREAM?

- AM I SEEING THIS PATTERN IN DIFFERENT WAYS IN OTHER DREAMS OR IN EVERYDAY LIFE? WHY IS THAT?

- IS GOD TRYING TO REALLY TELL ME SOMETHING?

How I felt:

Scripture:

What is God Saying?

**Date:**

**Dream:**

_____

_____

_____

_____

_____

_____

_____

_____

_____

_____

_____

_____

_____

_____

_____

_____

_____

_____

# DREAM CHECKLIST

## WHAT IS THE DREAM ABOUT?
## (TICK ALL THAT APPLY)

☐ ME

☐ SOMEONE ELSE

☐ A CORRECTION

☐ TO ENCOURAGE/BUILD FAITH

☐ REVEALING THE FUTURE

☐ OTHER

## SOME QUESTIONS TO ASK:

- WHAT COLOURS DID I SEE AND WHAT COULD THEY REPRESENT?

- HOW DID I FEEL WHEN I WOKE UP? HOW DID I FEEL IN THE DREAM?

- WHAT DOES THAT SYMBOLISE TO ME PERSONALLY?

- IS THERE A SCRIPTURE I CAN CONNECT TO MY DREAM?

- ARE THERE ANY REFERENCES IN SCRIPTURE TO THIS SYMBOL THAT MAY HELP ME INTERPRET MY DREAM?

- AM I SEEING THIS PATTERN IN DIFFERENT WAYS IN OTHER DREAMS OR IN EVERYDAY LIFE? WHY IS THAT?

- IS GOD TRYING TO REALLY TELL ME SOMETHING?

How I felt:

Scripture:

What is God Saying?

**Date:**

**Dream:**

_____

_____

_____

_____

_____

_____

_____

_____

_____

_____

_____

_____

_____

_____

_____

_____

_____

_____

_____

_____

# DREAM CHECKLIST

## WHAT IS THE DREAM ABOUT?
### (TICK ALL THAT APPLY)

- ☐ ME
- ☐ SOMEONE ELSE
- ☐ A CORRECTION
- ☐ TO ENCOURAGE/BUILD FAITH
- ☐ REVEALING THE FUTURE
- ☐ OTHER

## SOME QUESTIONS TO ASK:

- WHAT COLOURS DID I SEE AND WHAT COULD THEY REPRESENT?

- HOW DID I FEEL WHEN I WOKE UP? HOW DID I FEEL IN THE DREAM?

- WHAT DOES THAT SYMBOLISE TO ME PERSONALLY?

- IS THERE A SCRIPTURE I CAN CONNECT TO MY DREAM?

- ARE THERE ANY REFERENCES IN SCRIPTURE TO THIS SYMBOL THAT MAY HELP ME INTERPRET MY DREAM?

- AM I SEEING THIS PATTERN IN DIFFERENT WAYS IN OTHER DREAMS OR IN EVERYDAY LIFE? WHY IS THAT?

- IS GOD TRYING TO REALLY TELL ME SOMETHING?

How I felt:

Scripture:

What is God Saying?

Date:

Dream:

_____
_____
_____
_____
_____
_____
_____
_____
_____
_____
_____
_____
_____
_____
_____
_____
_____
_____

# DREAM CHECKLIST

## WHAT IS THE DREAM ABOUT?
### (TICK ALL THAT APPLY)

- ☐ ME
- ☐ SOMEONE ELSE
- ☐ A CORRECTION
- ☐ TO ENCOURAGE/BUILD FAITH
- ☐ REVEALING THE FUTURE
- ☐ OTHER

## SOME QUESTIONS TO ASK:

- WHAT COLOURS DID I SEE AND WHAT COULD THEY REPRESENT?

- HOW DID I FEEL WHEN I WOKE UP? HOW DID I FEEL IN THE DREAM?

- WHAT DOES THAT SYMBOLISE TO ME PERSONALLY?

- IS THERE A SCRIPTURE I CAN CONNECT TO MY DREAM?

- ARE THERE ANY REFERENCES IN SCRIPTURE TO THIS SYMBOL THAT MAY HELP ME INTERPRET MY DREAM?

- AM I SEEING THIS PATTERN IN DIFFERENT WAYS IN OTHER DREAMS OR IN EVERYDAY LIFE? WHY IS THAT?

- IS GOD TRYING TO REALLY TELL ME SOMETHING?

How I felt:

Scripture:

What is God Saying?

Date:

Dream:

_____
_____
_____
_____
_____
_____
_____
_____
_____
_____
_____
_____
_____
_____
_____
_____
_____
_____

# DREAM CHECKLIST

## WHAT IS THE DREAM ABOUT?
### (TICK ALL THAT APPLY)

- ☐ ME
- ☐ SOMEONE ELSE
- ☐ A CORRECTION
- ☐ TO ENCOURAGE/BUILD FAITH
- ☐ REVEALING THE FUTURE
- ☐ OTHER

## SOME QUESTIONS TO ASK:

- WHAT COLOURS DID I SEE AND WHAT COULD THEY REPRESENT?

- HOW DID I FEEL WHEN I WOKE UP? HOW DID I FEEL IN THE DREAM?

- WHAT DOES THAT SYMBOLISE TO ME PERSONALLY?

- IS THERE A SCRIPTURE I CAN CONNECT TO MY DREAM?

- ARE THERE ANY REFERENCES IN SCRIPTURE TO THIS SYMBOL THAT MAY HELP ME INTERPRET MY DREAM?

- AM I SEEING THIS PATTERN IN DIFFERENT WAYS IN OTHER DREAMS OR IN EVERYDAY LIFE? WHY IS THAT?

- IS GOD TRYING TO REALLY TELL ME SOMETHING?

How I felt:

Scripture:

What is God Saying?

**Date:**

**Dream:**

_____

_____

_____

_____

_____

_____

_____

_____

_____

_____

_____

_____

_____

_____

_____

_____

_____

_____

_____

_____

_____

# DREAM CHECKLIST

## WHAT IS THE DREAM ABOUT?
### (TICK ALL THAT APPLY)

- ☐ ME
- ☐ SOMEONE ELSE
- ☐ A CORRECTION
- ☐ TO ENCOURAGE/BUILD FAITH
- ☐ REVEALING THE FUTURE
- ☐ OTHER

## SOME QUESTIONS TO ASK:

- WHAT COLOURS DID I SEE AND WHAT COULD THEY REPRESENT?

- HOW DID I FEEL WHEN I WOKE UP? HOW DID I FEEL IN THE DREAM?

- WHAT DOES THAT SYMBOLISE TO ME PERSONALLY?

- IS THERE A SCRIPTURE I CAN CONNECT TO MY DREAM?

- ARE THERE ANY REFERENCES IN SCRIPTURE TO THIS SYMBOL THAT MAY HELP ME INTERPRET MY DREAM?

- AM I SEEING THIS PATTERN IN DIFFERENT WAYS IN OTHER DREAMS OR IN EVERYDAY LIFE? WHY IS THAT?

- IS GOD TRYING TO REALLY TELL ME SOMETHING?

How I felt:

Scripture:

What is God Saying?

**Date:**

**Dream:**

_____

_____

_____

_____

_____

_____

_____

_____

_____

_____

_____

_____

_____

_____

_____

_____

_____

_____

_____

_____

# DREAM CHECKLIST

## WHAT IS THE DREAM ABOUT?
### (TICK ALL THAT APPLY)

- ☐ ME
- ☐ SOMEONE ELSE
- ☐ A CORRECTION
- ☐ TO ENCOURAGE/BUILD FAITH
- ☐ REVEALING THE FUTURE
- ☐ OTHER

## SOME QUESTIONS TO ASK:

- WHAT COLOURS DID I SEE AND WHAT COULD THEY REPRESENT?

- HOW DID I FEEL WHEN I WOKE UP? HOW DID I FEEL IN THE DREAM?

- WHAT DOES THAT SYMBOLISE TO ME PERSONALLY?

- IS THERE A SCRIPTURE I CAN CONNECT TO MY DREAM?

- ARE THERE ANY REFERENCES IN SCRIPTURE TO THIS SYMBOL THAT MAY HELP ME INTERPRET MY DREAM?

- AM I SEEING THIS PATTERN IN DIFFERENT WAYS IN OTHER DREAMS OR IN EVERYDAY LIFE? WHY IS THAT?

- IS GOD TRYING TO REALLY TELL ME SOMETHING?

How I felt:

Scripture:

What is God Saying?

**Date:**

**Dream:**

# DREAM CHECKLIST

## WHAT IS THE DREAM ABOUT?
### (TICK ALL THAT APPLY)

- ☐ ME
- ☐ SOMEONE ELSE
- ☐ A CORRECTION
- ☐ TO ENCOURAGE/BUILD FAITH
- ☐ REVEALING THE FUTURE
- ☐ OTHER

## SOME QUESTIONS TO ASK:

- WHAT COLOURS DID I SEE AND WHAT COULD THEY REPRESENT?

- HOW DID I FEEL WHEN I WOKE UP? HOW DID I FEEL IN THE DREAM?

- WHAT DOES THAT SYMBOLISE TO ME PERSONALLY?

- IS THERE A SCRIPTURE I CAN CONNECT TO MY DREAM?

- ARE THERE ANY REFERENCES IN SCRIPTURE TO THIS SYMBOL THAT MAY HELP ME INTERPRET MY DREAM?

- AM I SEEING THIS PATTERN IN DIFFERENT WAYS IN OTHER DREAMS OR IN EVERYDAY LIFE? WHY IS THAT?

- IS GOD TRYING TO REALLY TELL ME SOMETHING?

How I felt:

Scripture:

What is God Saying?

**Date:**

**Dream:**

# DREAM CHECKLIST

## WHAT IS THE DREAM ABOUT?
### (TICK ALL THAT APPLY)

- [ ] ME
- [ ] SOMEONE ELSE
- [ ] A CORRECTION
- [ ] TO ENCOURAGE/BUILD FAITH
- [ ] REVEALING THE FUTURE
- [ ] OTHER

## SOME QUESTIONS TO ASK:

- WHAT COLOURS DID I SEE AND WHAT COULD THEY REPRESENT?

- HOW DID I FEEL WHEN I WOKE UP? HOW DID I FEEL IN THE DREAM?

- WHAT DOES THAT SYMBOLISE TO ME PERSONALLY?

- IS THERE A SCRIPTURE I CAN CONNECT TO MY DREAM?

- ARE THERE ANY REFERENCES IN SCRIPTURE TO THIS SYMBOL THAT MAY HELP ME INTERPRET MY DREAM?

- AM I SEEING THIS PATTERN IN DIFFERENT WAYS IN OTHER DREAMS OR IN EVERYDAY LIFE? WHY IS THAT?

- IS GOD TRYING TO REALLY TELL ME SOMETHING?

How I felt:

Scripture:

What is God Saying?

Date:

Dream:

_____

_____

_____

_____

_____

_____

_____

_____

_____

_____

_____

_____

_____

_____

_____

_____

_____

_____

# DREAM CHECKLIST

## WHAT IS THE DREAM ABOUT?
### (TICK ALL THAT APPLY)

- ☐ ME
- ☐ SOMEONE ELSE
- ☐ A CORRECTION
- ☐ TO ENCOURAGE/BUILD FAITH
- ☐ REVEALING THE FUTURE
- ☐ OTHER

## SOME QUESTIONS TO ASK:

- WHAT COLOURS DID I SEE AND WHAT COULD THEY REPRESENT?

- HOW DID I FEEL WHEN I WOKE UP? HOW DID I FEEL IN THE DREAM?

- WHAT DOES THAT SYMBOLISE TO ME PERSONALLY?

- IS THERE A SCRIPTURE I CAN CONNECT TO MY DREAM?

- ARE THERE ANY REFERENCES IN SCRIPTURE TO THIS SYMBOL THAT MAY HELP ME INTERPRET MY DREAM?

- AM I SEEING THIS PATTERN IN DIFFERENT WAYS IN OTHER DREAMS OR IN EVERYDAY LIFE? WHY IS THAT?

- IS GOD TRYING TO REALLY TELL ME SOMETHING?

How I felt:

Scripture:

What is God Saying?

**Date:**

**Dream:**

# DREAM CHECKLIST

## WHAT IS THE DREAM ABOUT?
### (TICK ALL THAT APPLY)

- ☐ ME
- ☐ SOMEONE ELSE
- ☐ A CORRECTION
- ☐ TO ENCOURAGE/BUILD FAITH
- ☐ REVEALING THE FUTURE
- ☐ OTHER

## SOME QUESTIONS TO ASK:

- WHAT COLOURS DID I SEE AND WHAT COULD THEY REPRESENT?

- HOW DID I FEEL WHEN I WOKE UP? HOW DID I FEEL IN THE DREAM?

- WHAT DOES THAT SYMBOLISE TO ME PERSONALLY?

- IS THERE A SCRIPTURE I CAN CONNECT TO MY DREAM?

- ARE THERE ANY REFERENCES IN SCRIPTURE TO THIS SYMBOL THAT MAY HELP ME INTERPRET MY DREAM?

- AM I SEEING THIS PATTERN IN DIFFERENT WAYS IN OTHER DREAMS OR IN EVERYDAY LIFE? WHY IS THAT?

- IS GOD TRYING TO REALLY TELL ME SOMETHING?

How I felt:

Scripture:

What is God Saying?

Date:

Dream:

_____

_____

_____

_____

_____

_____

_____

_____

_____

_____

_____

_____

_____

_____

# DREAM CHECKLIST

## WHAT IS THE DREAM ABOUT?
### (TICK ALL THAT APPLY)

- ☐ ME
- ☐ SOMEONE ELSE
- ☐ A CORRECTION
- ☐ TO ENCOURAGE/BUILD FAITH
- ☐ REVEALING THE FUTURE
- ☐ OTHER

## SOME QUESTIONS TO ASK:

- WHAT COLOURS DID I SEE AND WHAT COULD THEY REPRESENT?

- HOW DID I FEEL WHEN I WOKE UP? HOW DID I FEEL IN THE DREAM?

- WHAT DOES THAT SYMBOLISE TO ME PERSONALLY?

- IS THERE A SCRIPTURE I CAN CONNECT TO MY DREAM?

- ARE THERE ANY REFERENCES IN SCRIPTURE TO THIS SYMBOL THAT MAY HELP ME INTERPRET MY DREAM?

- AM I SEEING THIS PATTERN IN DIFFERENT WAYS IN OTHER DREAMS OR IN EVERYDAY LIFE? WHY IS THAT?

- IS GOD TRYING TO REALLY TELL ME SOMETHING?

How I felt:

Scripture:

What is God Saying?

**Date:**

**Dream:**

_____
_____
_____
_____
_____
_____
_____
_____
_____
_____
_____
_____
_____
_____
_____
_____
_____
_____

# DREAM CHECKLIST

## WHAT IS THE DREAM ABOUT?
### (TICK ALL THAT APPLY)

- ☐ ME
- ☐ SOMEONE ELSE
- ☐ A CORRECTION
- ☐ TO ENCOURAGE/BUILD FAITH
- ☐ REVEALING THE FUTURE
- ☐ OTHER

## SOME QUESTIONS TO ASK:

- WHAT COLOURS DID I SEE AND WHAT COULD THEY REPRESENT?

- HOW DID I FEEL WHEN I WOKE UP? HOW DID I FEEL IN THE DREAM?

- WHAT DOES THAT SYMBOLISE TO ME PERSONALLY?

- IS THERE A SCRIPTURE I CAN CONNECT TO MY DREAM?

- ARE THERE ANY REFERENCES IN SCRIPTURE TO THIS SYMBOL THAT MAY HELP ME INTERPRET MY DREAM?

- AM I SEEING THIS PATTERN IN DIFFERENT WAYS IN OTHER DREAMS OR IN EVERYDAY LIFE? WHY IS THAT?

- IS GOD TRYING TO REALLY TELL ME SOMETHING?

How I felt:

Scripture:

What is God Saying?

**Date:**

**Dream:**

# DREAM CHECKLIST

## WHAT IS THE DREAM ABOUT?
### (TICK ALL THAT APPLY)

- ☐ ME
- ☐ SOMEONE ELSE
- ☐ A CORRECTION
- ☐ TO ENCOURAGE/BUILD FAITH
- ☐ REVEALING THE FUTURE
- ☐ OTHER

## SOME QUESTIONS TO ASK:

- WHAT COLOURS DID I SEE AND WHAT COULD THEY REPRESENT?

- HOW DID I FEEL WHEN I WOKE UP? HOW DID I FEEL IN THE DREAM?

- WHAT DOES THAT SYMBOLISE TO ME PERSONALLY?

- IS THERE A SCRIPTURE I CAN CONNECT TO MY DREAM?

- ARE THERE ANY REFERENCES IN SCRIPTURE TO THIS SYMBOL THAT MAY HELP ME INTERPRET MY DREAM?

- AM I SEEING THIS PATTERN IN DIFFERENT WAYS IN OTHER DREAMS OR IN EVERYDAY LIFE? WHY IS THAT?

- IS GOD TRYING TO REALLY TELL ME SOMETHING?

How I felt:

Scripture:

What is God Saying?

Date:

Dream:

_____

_____

_____

_____

_____

_____

_____

_____

_____

_____

_____

_____

_____

_____

_____

_____

_____

_____

_____

_____

_____

# DREAM CHECKLIST

## WHAT IS THE DREAM ABOUT?
### (TICK ALL THAT APPLY)

☐ ME

☐ SOMEONE ELSE

☐ A CORRECTION

☐ TO ENCOURAGE/BUILD FAITH

☐ REVEALING THE FUTURE

☐ OTHER

## SOME QUESTIONS TO ASK:

- WHAT COLOURS DID I SEE AND WHAT COULD THEY REPRESENT?

- HOW DID I FEEL WHEN I WOKE UP? HOW DID I FEEL IN THE DREAM?

- WHAT DOES THAT SYMBOLISE TO ME PERSONALLY?

- IS THERE A SCRIPTURE I CAN CONNECT TO MY DREAM?

- ARE THERE ANY REFERENCES IN SCRIPTURE TO THIS SYMBOL THAT MAY HELP ME INTERPRET MY DREAM?

- AM I SEEING THIS PATTERN IN DIFFERENT WAYS IN OTHER DREAMS OR IN EVERYDAY LIFE? WHY IS THAT?

- IS GOD TRYING TO REALLY TELL ME SOMETHING?

How I felt:

Scripture:

What is God Saying?

**Date:**

**Dream:**

# DREAM CHECKLIST

## WHAT IS THE DREAM ABOUT?
### (TICK ALL THAT APPLY)

- ☐ ME
- ☐ SOMEONE ELSE
- ☐ A CORRECTION
- ☐ TO ENCOURAGE/BUILD FAITH
- ☐ REVEALING THE FUTURE
- ☐ OTHER

## SOME QUESTIONS TO ASK:

- WHAT COLOURS DID I SEE AND WHAT COULD THEY REPRESENT?

- HOW DID I FEEL WHEN I WOKE UP? HOW DID I FEEL IN THE DREAM?

- WHAT DOES THAT SYMBOLISE TO ME PERSONALLY?

- IS THERE A SCRIPTURE I CAN CONNECT TO MY DREAM?

- ARE THERE ANY REFERENCES IN SCRIPTURE TO THIS SYMBOL THAT MAY HELP ME INTERPRET MY DREAM?

- AM I SEEING THIS PATTERN IN DIFFERENT WAYS IN OTHER DREAMS OR IN EVERYDAY LIFE? WHY IS THAT?

- IS GOD TRYING TO REALLY TELL ME SOMETHING?

How I felt:

Scripture:

What is God Saying?

**Date:**

**Dream:**

_____

_____

_____

_____

_____

_____

_____

_____

_____

_____

_____

_____

_____

_____

_____

_____

# DREAM CHECKLIST

## WHAT IS THE DREAM ABOUT?
## (TICK ALL THAT APPLY)

- ☐ ME
- ☐ SOMEONE ELSE
- ☐ A CORRECTION
- ☐ TO ENCOURAGE/BUILD FAITH
- ☐ REVEALING THE FUTURE
- ☐ OTHER

## SOME QUESTIONS TO ASK:

- WHAT COLOURS DID I SEE AND WHAT COULD THEY REPRESENT?

- HOW DID I FEEL WHEN I WOKE UP? HOW DID I FEEL IN THE DREAM?

- WHAT DOES THAT SYMBOLISE TO ME PERSONALLY?

- IS THERE A SCRIPTURE I CAN CONNECT TO MY DREAM?

- ARE THERE ANY REFERENCES IN SCRIPTURE TO THIS SYMBOL THAT MAY HELP ME INTERPRET MY DREAM?

- AM I SEEING THIS PATTERN IN DIFFERENT WAYS IN OTHER DREAMS OR IN EVERYDAY LIFE? WHY IS THAT?

- IS GOD TRYING TO REALLY TELL ME SOMETHING?

How I felt:

Scripture:

What is God Saying?

Date:

Dream:

# DREAM CHECKLIST

## WHAT IS THE DREAM ABOUT?
### (TICK ALL THAT APPLY)

- ☐ ME
- ☐ SOMEONE ELSE
- ☐ A CORRECTION
- ☐ TO ENCOURAGE/BUILD FAITH
- ☐ REVEALING THE FUTURE
- ☐ OTHER

## SOME QUESTIONS TO ASK:

- WHAT COLOURS DID I SEE AND WHAT COULD THEY REPRESENT?

- HOW DID I FEEL WHEN I WOKE UP? HOW DID I FEEL IN THE DREAM?

- WHAT DOES THAT SYMBOLISE TO ME PERSONALLY?

- IS THERE A SCRIPTURE I CAN CONNECT TO MY DREAM?

- ARE THERE ANY REFERENCES IN SCRIPTURE TO THIS SYMBOL THAT MAY HELP ME INTERPRET MY DREAM?

- AM I SEEING THIS PATTERN IN DIFFERENT WAYS IN OTHER DREAMS OR IN EVERYDAY LIFE? WHY IS THAT?

- IS GOD TRYING TO REALLY TELL ME SOMETHING?

How I felt:

Scripture:

What is God Saying?

**Date:**

**Dream:**

_____

_____

_____

_____

_____

_____

_____

_____

_____

_____

_____

_____

_____

_____

_____

_____

_____

_____

_____

# DREAM CHECKLIST

## WHAT IS THE DREAM ABOUT?
### (TICK ALL THAT APPLY)

- [ ] ME
- [ ] SOMEONE ELSE
- [ ] A CORRECTION
- [ ] TO ENCOURAGE/BUILD FAITH
- [ ] REVEALING THE FUTURE
- [ ] OTHER

## SOME QUESTIONS TO ASK:

- WHAT COLOURS DID I SEE AND WHAT COULD THEY REPRESENT?

- HOW DID I FEEL WHEN I WOKE UP? HOW DID I FEEL IN THE DREAM?

- WHAT DOES THAT SYMBOLISE TO ME PERSONALLY?

- IS THERE A SCRIPTURE I CAN CONNECT TO MY DREAM?

- ARE THERE ANY REFERENCES IN SCRIPTURE TO THIS SYMBOL THAT MAY HELP ME INTERPRET MY DREAM?

- AM I SEEING THIS PATTERN IN DIFFERENT WAYS IN OTHER DREAMS OR IN EVERYDAY LIFE? WHY IS THAT?

- IS GOD TRYING TO REALLY TELL ME SOMETHING?

How I felt:

Scripture:

What is God Saying?

**Date:**

**Dream:**

_____

_____

_____

_____

_____

_____

_____

_____

_____

_____

_____

_____

_____

_____

_____

_____

_____

_____

# DREAM CHECKLIST

## WHAT IS THE DREAM ABOUT?
### (TICK ALL THAT APPLY)

☐ ME

☐ SOMEONE ELSE

☐ A CORRECTION

☐ TO ENCOURAGE/BUILD FAITH

☐ REVEALING THE FUTURE

☐ OTHER

## SOME QUESTIONS TO ASK:

- WHAT COLOURS DID I SEE AND WHAT COULD THEY REPRESENT?

- HOW DID I FEEL WHEN I WOKE UP? HOW DID I FEEL IN THE DREAM?

- WHAT DOES THAT SYMBOLISE TO ME PERSONALLY?

- IS THERE A SCRIPTURE I CAN CONNECT TO MY DREAM?

- ARE THERE ANY REFERENCES IN SCRIPTURE TO THIS SYMBOL THAT MAY HELP ME INTERPRET MY DREAM?

- AM I SEEING THIS PATTERN IN DIFFERENT WAYS IN OTHER DREAMS OR IN EVERYDAY LIFE? WHY IS THAT?

- IS GOD TRYING TO REALLY TELL ME SOMETHING?

How I felt:

Scripture:

What is God Saying?

**Date:**

**Dream:**

_____
_____
_____
_____
_____
_____
_____
_____
_____
_____
_____
_____
_____
_____
_____
_____
_____
_____
_____
_____
_____
_____
_____

# DREAM CHECKLIST

## WHAT IS THE DREAM ABOUT?
### (TICK ALL THAT APPLY)

- ☐ ME
- ☐ SOMEONE ELSE
- ☐ A CORRECTION
- ☐ TO ENCOURAGE/BUILD FAITH
- ☐ REVEALING THE FUTURE
- ☐ OTHER

## SOME QUESTIONS TO ASK:

- WHAT COLOURS DID I SEE AND WHAT COULD THEY REPRESENT?

- HOW DID I FEEL WHEN I WOKE UP? HOW DID I FEEL IN THE DREAM?

- WHAT DOES THAT SYMBOLISE TO ME PERSONALLY?

- IS THERE A SCRIPTURE I CAN CONNECT TO MY DREAM?

- ARE THERE ANY REFERENCES IN SCRIPTURE TO THIS SYMBOL THAT MAY HELP ME INTERPRET MY DREAM?

- AM I SEEING THIS PATTERN IN DIFFERENT WAYS IN OTHER DREAMS OR IN EVERYDAY LIFE? WHY IS THAT?

- IS GOD TRYING TO REALLY TELL ME SOMETHING?

How I felt:

Scripture:

What is God Saying?

Date:

Dream:

_____

_____

_____

_____

_____

_____

_____

_____

_____

_____

_____

_____

_____

_____

_____

_____

_____

_____

_____

# DREAM CHECKLIST

## WHAT IS THE DREAM ABOUT?
### (TICK ALL THAT APPLY)

- ☐ ME
- ☐ SOMEONE ELSE
- ☐ A CORRECTION
- ☐ TO ENCOURAGE/BUILD FAITH
- ☐ REVEALING THE FUTURE
- ☐ OTHER

## SOME QUESTIONS TO ASK:

- WHAT COLOURS DID I SEE AND WHAT COULD THEY REPRESENT?

- HOW DID I FEEL WHEN I WOKE UP? HOW DID I FEEL IN THE DREAM?

- WHAT DOES THAT SYMBOLISE TO ME PERSONALLY?

- IS THERE A SCRIPTURE I CAN CONNECT TO MY DREAM?

- ARE THERE ANY REFERENCES IN SCRIPTURE TO THIS SYMBOL THAT MAY HELP ME INTERPRET MY DREAM?

- AM I SEEING THIS PATTERN IN DIFFERENT WAYS IN OTHER DREAMS OR IN EVERYDAY LIFE? WHY IS THAT?

- IS GOD TRYING TO REALLY TELL ME SOMETHING?

How I felt:

Scripture:

What is God Saying?

**Date:**

**Dream:**

# DREAM CHECKLIST

## WHAT IS THE DREAM ABOUT?
### (TICK ALL THAT APPLY)

- ☐ ME
- ☐ SOMEONE ELSE
- ☐ A CORRECTION
- ☐ TO ENCOURAGE/BUILD FAITH
- ☐ REVEALING THE FUTURE
- ☐ OTHER

## SOME QUESTIONS TO ASK:

- WHAT COLOURS DID I SEE AND WHAT COULD THEY REPRESENT?

- HOW DID I FEEL WHEN I WOKE UP? HOW DID I FEEL IN THE DREAM?

- WHAT DOES THAT SYMBOLISE TO ME PERSONALLY?

- IS THERE A SCRIPTURE I CAN CONNECT TO MY DREAM?

- ARE THERE ANY REFERENCES IN SCRIPTURE TO THIS SYMBOL THAT MAY HELP ME INTERPRET MY DREAM?

- AM I SEEING THIS PATTERN IN DIFFERENT WAYS IN OTHER DREAMS OR IN EVERYDAY LIFE? WHY IS THAT?

- IS GOD TRYING TO REALLY TELL ME SOMETHING?

How I felt:

Scripture:

What is God Saying?

Date:

Dream:

_____
_____
_____
_____
_____
_____
_____
_____
_____
_____
_____
_____
_____
_____
_____
_____
_____
_____
_____
_____
_____
_____

# DREAM CHECKLIST

## WHAT IS THE DREAM ABOUT?
### (TICK ALL THAT APPLY)

- ☐ ME
- ☐ SOMEONE ELSE
- ☐ A CORRECTION
- ☐ TO ENCOURAGE/BUILD FAITH
- ☐ REVEALING THE FUTURE
- ☐ OTHER

## SOME QUESTIONS TO ASK:

- WHAT COLOURS DID I SEE AND WHAT COULD THEY REPRESENT?

- HOW DID I FEEL WHEN I WOKE UP? HOW DID I FEEL IN THE DREAM?

- WHAT DOES THAT SYMBOLISE TO ME PERSONALLY?

- IS THERE A SCRIPTURE I CAN CONNECT TO MY DREAM?

- ARE THERE ANY REFERENCES IN SCRIPTURE TO THIS SYMBOL THAT MAY HELP ME INTERPRET MY DREAM?

- AM I SEEING THIS PATTERN IN DIFFERENT WAYS IN OTHER DREAMS OR IN EVERYDAY LIFE? WHY IS THAT?

- IS GOD TRYING TO REALLY TELL ME SOMETHING?

How I felt:

Scripture:

What is God Saying?

**Date:**

**Dream:**

# DREAM CHECKLIST

## WHAT IS THE DREAM ABOUT?
### (TICK ALL THAT APPLY)

- ☐ ME
- ☐ SOMEONE ELSE
- ☐ A CORRECTION
- ☐ TO ENCOURAGE/BUILD FAITH
- ☐ REVEALING THE FUTURE
- ☐ OTHER

## SOME QUESTIONS TO ASK:

- WHAT COLOURS DID I SEE AND WHAT COULD THEY REPRESENT?

- HOW DID I FEEL WHEN I WOKE UP? HOW DID I FEEL IN THE DREAM?

- WHAT DOES THAT SYMBOLISE TO ME PERSONALLY?

- IS THERE A SCRIPTURE I CAN CONNECT TO MY DREAM?

- ARE THERE ANY REFERENCES IN SCRIPTURE TO THIS SYMBOL THAT MAY HELP ME INTERPRET MY DREAM?

- AM I SEEING THIS PATTERN IN DIFFERENT WAYS IN OTHER DREAMS OR IN EVERYDAY LIFE? WHY IS THAT?

- IS GOD TRYING TO REALLY TELL ME SOMETHING?

How I felt:

Scripture:

What is God Saying?

Date:

Dream:

_____
_____
_____
_____
_____
_____
_____
_____
_____
_____
_____
_____
_____
_____
_____
_____
_____
_____
_____

# DREAM CHECKLIST

## WHAT IS THE DREAM ABOUT?
### (TICK ALL THAT APPLY)

- ☐ ME
- ☐ SOMEONE ELSE
- ☐ A CORRECTION
- ☐ TO ENCOURAGE/BUILD FAITH
- ☐ REVEALING THE FUTURE
- ☐ OTHER

## SOME QUESTIONS TO ASK:

- WHAT COLOURS DID I SEE AND WHAT COULD THEY REPRESENT?

- HOW DID I FEEL WHEN I WOKE UP? HOW DID I FEEL IN THE DREAM?

- WHAT DOES THAT SYMBOLISE TO ME PERSONALLY?

- IS THERE A SCRIPTURE I CAN CONNECT TO MY DREAM?

- ARE THERE ANY REFERENCES IN SCRIPTURE TO THIS SYMBOL THAT MAY HELP ME INTERPRET MY DREAM?

- AM I SEEING THIS PATTERN IN DIFFERENT WAYS IN OTHER DREAMS OR IN EVERYDAY LIFE? WHY IS THAT?

- IS GOD TRYING TO REALLY TELL ME SOMETHING?

How I felt:

Scripture:

What is God Saying?

Date:

Dream:

_____
_____
_____
_____
_____
_____
_____
_____
_____
_____
_____
_____
_____
_____
_____
_____
_____
_____
_____
_____

# DREAM CHECKLIST

## WHAT IS THE DREAM ABOUT?
### (TICK ALL THAT APPLY)

- [ ] ME
- [ ] SOMEONE ELSE
- [ ] A CORRECTION
- [ ] TO ENCOURAGE/BUILD FAITH
- [ ] REVEALING THE FUTURE
- [ ] OTHER

## SOME QUESTIONS TO ASK:

- WHAT COLOURS DID I SEE AND WHAT COULD THEY REPRESENT?

- HOW DID I FEEL WHEN I WOKE UP? HOW DID I FEEL IN THE DREAM?

- WHAT DOES THAT SYMBOLISE TO ME PERSONALLY?

- IS THERE A SCRIPTURE I CAN CONNECT TO MY DREAM?

- ARE THERE ANY REFERENCES IN SCRIPTURE TO THIS SYMBOL THAT MAY HELP ME INTERPRET MY DREAM?

- AM I SEEING THIS PATTERN IN DIFFERENT WAYS IN OTHER DREAMS OR IN EVERYDAY LIFE? WHY IS THAT?

- IS GOD TRYING TO REALLY TELL ME SOMETHING?

How I felt:

Scripture:

What is God Saying?

Date:

Dream:

_____

_____

_____

_____

_____

_____

_____

_____

_____

_____

_____

_____

_____

_____

_____

_____

_____

_____

_____

_____

# DREAM CHECKLIST

## WHAT IS THE DREAM ABOUT?
### (TICK ALL THAT APPLY)

- ☐ ME
- ☐ SOMEONE ELSE
- ☐ A CORRECTION
- ☐ TO ENCOURAGE/BUILD FAITH
- ☐ REVEALING THE FUTURE
- ☐ OTHER

## SOME QUESTIONS TO ASK:

- WHAT COLOURS DID I SEE AND WHAT COULD THEY REPRESENT?

- HOW DID I FEEL WHEN I WOKE UP? HOW DID I FEEL IN THE DREAM?

- WHAT DOES THAT SYMBOLISE TO ME PERSONALLY?

- IS THERE A SCRIPTURE I CAN CONNECT TO MY DREAM?

- ARE THERE ANY REFERENCES IN SCRIPTURE TO THIS SYMBOL THAT MAY HELP ME INTERPRET MY DREAM?

- AM I SEEING THIS PATTERN IN DIFFERENT WAYS IN OTHER DREAMS OR IN EVERYDAY LIFE? WHY IS THAT?

- IS GOD TRYING TO REALLY TELL ME SOMETHING?

How I felt:

Scripture:

What is God Saying?

Date:

Dream:

_____

_____

_____

_____

_____

_____

_____

_____

_____

_____

_____

_____

_____

_____

_____

_____

_____

# DREAM CHECKLIST

## WHAT IS THE DREAM ABOUT?
### (TICK ALL THAT APPLY)

- ☐ ME
- ☐ SOMEONE ELSE
- ☐ A CORRECTION
- ☐ TO ENCOURAGE/BUILD FAITH
- ☐ REVEALING THE FUTURE
- ☐ OTHER

## SOME QUESTIONS TO ASK:

- WHAT COLOURS DID I SEE AND WHAT COULD THEY REPRESENT?

- HOW DID I FEEL WHEN I WOKE UP? HOW DID I FEEL IN THE DREAM?

- WHAT DOES THAT SYMBOLISE TO ME PERSONALLY?

- IS THERE A SCRIPTURE I CAN CONNECT TO MY DREAM?

- ARE THERE ANY REFERENCES IN SCRIPTURE TO THIS SYMBOL THAT MAY HELP ME INTERPRET MY DREAM?

- AM I SEEING THIS PATTERN IN DIFFERENT WAYS IN OTHER DREAMS OR IN EVERYDAY LIFE? WHY IS THAT?

- IS GOD TRYING TO REALLY TELL ME SOMETHING?

How I felt:

Scripture:

What is God Saying?

Date:

Dream:

_____
_____
_____
_____
_____
_____
_____
_____
_____
_____
_____
_____
_____
_____
_____
_____
_____
_____

# DREAM CHECKLIST

## WHAT IS THE DREAM ABOUT?
### (TICK ALL THAT APPLY)

- ☐ ME
- ☐ SOMEONE ELSE
- ☐ A CORRECTION
- ☐ TO ENCOURAGE/BUILD FAITH
- ☐ REVEALING THE FUTURE
- ☐ OTHER

## SOME QUESTIONS TO ASK:

- WHAT COLOURS DID I SEE AND WHAT COULD THEY REPRESENT?

- HOW DID I FEEL WHEN I WOKE UP? HOW DID I FEEL IN THE DREAM?

- WHAT DOES THAT SYMBOLISE TO ME PERSONALLY?

- IS THERE A SCRIPTURE I CAN CONNECT TO MY DREAM?

- ARE THERE ANY REFERENCES IN SCRIPTURE TO THIS SYMBOL THAT MAY HELP ME INTERPRET MY DREAM?

- AM I SEEING THIS PATTERN IN DIFFERENT WAYS IN OTHER DREAMS OR IN EVERYDAY LIFE? WHY IS THAT?

- IS GOD TRYING TO REALLY TELL ME SOMETHING?

How I felt:

Scripture:

What is God Saying?

CPSIA information can be obtained
at www.ICGtesting.com
Printed in the USA
LVHW070700161221
706367LV00004B/58